MW00699711

This book belongs to:

_____

This book is dedicated
to magical creatures everywhere.

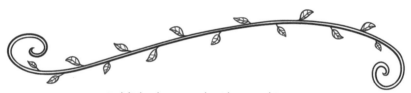

Published in 2019 by Flowered Press
Copyright 2019 by Hayley Rose

Text and design by Hayley Rose
Illustrations by Lynx Animation Studios

ISBN: 978-0-9998073-2-3
Library of Congress Cataloging-in-Publication Process

Printed in China

The Thankful Unicorn:

Release Your Inner Magic

By Hayley Rose

Illustrated by Lynx Animation Studios

Date _____

Today I am thankful for:

1. _____
2. _____
3. _____

My dreams and goals:

1. _____
2. _____
3. _____

What I love about myself:

1. _____
2. _____
3. _____

My affirmations:

1. _____
2. _____
3. _____

"He is greatest whose strength carries up the most hearts by attraction of his own."
~ Henry Ward Beecher

Date _____

Today I am thankful for:

1. _____
2. _____
3. _____

My dreams and goals:

1. _____
2. _____
3. _____

What I love about myself:

1. _____
2. _____
3. _____

My affirmations:

1. _____
2. _____
3. _____

"Gratitude is the fairest blossom which springs from the soul.
~ Henry Ward Beecher

Date _____

Today I am thankful for:

1. _____
2. _____
3. _____

My dreams and goals:

1. _____
2. _____
3. _____

What I love about myself:

1. _____
2. _____
3. _____

My affirmations:

1. _____
2. _____
3. _____

"No duty is more urgent than that of returning thanks." ~ James Allen

Date _____

Today I am thankful for:

1. _____

2. _____

3. _____

My dreams and goals:

1. _____

2. _____

3. _____

What I love about myself:

1. _____

2. _____

3. _____

My affirmations:

1. _____

2. _____

3. _____

"Let us be grateful to people who make us happy, they are the charming gardeners who make our souls blossom." ~ Marcel Proust

Date _____

Today I am thankful for:

1. _____
2. _____
3. _____

My dreams and goals:

1. _____
2. _____
3. _____

What I love about myself:

1. _____
2. _____
3. _____

My affirmations:

1. _____
2. _____
3. _____

"The essence of all beautiful art, all great art, is gratitude." ~ Friedrich Nietzsche

Date _____

Today I am thankful for:

1. _____
2. _____
3. _____

My dreams and goals:

1. _____
2. _____
3. _____

What I love about myself:

1. _____
2. _____
3. _____

My affirmations:

1. _____
2. _____
3. _____

"It's not what happens to you, but how you react to it that matters." ~ Epictetus

Date _____

Today I am thankful for:

1. _____
2. _____
3. _____

My dreams and goals:

1. _____
2. _____
3. _____

What I love about myself:

1. _____
2. _____
3. _____

My affirmations:

1. _____
2. _____
3. _____

"Happiness is a habit—cultivate it." ~ Elbert Hubbard

Date _____

Today I am thankful for:

1. _____
2. _____
3. _____

My dreams and goals:

1. _____
2. _____
3. _____

What I love about myself:

1. _____
2. _____
3. _____

My affirmations:

1. _____
2. _____
3. _____

"Wonder is the desire for knowledge." ~ Thomas Aquinas

Date _____

Today I am thankful for:

1. _____
2. _____
3. _____

My dreams and goals:

1. _____
2. _____
3. _____

What I love about myself:

1. _____
2. _____
3. _____

My affirmations:

1. _____
2. _____
3. _____

"You are today where your thoughts have brought you." ~ James Allen

Date _____

Today I am thankful for:

1. _____
2. _____
3. _____

My dreams and goals:

1. _____
2. _____
3. _____

What I love about myself:

1. _____
2. _____
3. _____

My affirmations:

1. _____
2. _____
3. _____

"A man is literally what he thinks." ~ James Allen

Date _____

Today I am thankful for:

1. _____
2. _____
3. _____

My dreams and goals:

1. _____
2. _____
3. _____

What I love about myself:

1. _____
2. _____
3. _____

My affirmations:

1. _____
2. _____
3. _____

"Dream lofty dreams, and as you dream, so you shall become, your vision is the promise of what you shall one day be." ~ James Allen

Date _____

Today I am thankful for:

1. _____
2. _____
3. _____

My dreams and goals:

1. _____
2. _____
3. _____

What I love about myself:

1. _____
2. _____
3. _____

My affirmations:

1. _____
2. _____
3. _____

"A person is only by the thoughts that he chooses." ~ James Allen

Date _____

Today I am thankful for:

1. _____
2. _____
3. _____

My dreams and goals:

1. _____
2. _____
3. _____

What I love about myself:

1. _____
2. _____
3. _____

My affirmations:

1. _____
2. _____
3. _____

"As a man thinketh in his heart, so shall he be." ~ James Allen

Date _____

Today I am thankful for:

1. _____

2. _____

3. _____

My dreams and goals:

1. _____

2. _____

3. _____

What I love about myself:

1. _____

2. _____

3. _____

My affirmations:

1. _____

2. _____

3. _____

"All that a man achieves and all that he fails to achieve is the direct result of his own thoughts." ~ James Allen

Date _____

Today I am thankful for:

1. _____
2. _____
3. _____

My dreams and goals:

1. _____
2. _____
3. _____

What I love about myself:

1. _____
2. _____
3. _____

My affirmations:

1. _____
2. _____
3. _____

"Our life is what our thoughts make it." ~ James Allen

Date _____

Today I am thankful for:

1. _____
2. _____
3. _____

My dreams and goals:

1. _____
2. _____
3. _____

What I love about myself:

1. _____
2. _____
3. _____

My affirmations:

1. _____
2. _____
3. _____

"He is greatest whose strength carries up the most hearts by attraction of his own."
~ Henry Ward Beecher

Date _____

Today I am thankful for:

1. _____
2. _____
3. _____

My dreams and goals:

1. _____
2. _____
3. _____

What I love about myself:

1. _____
2. _____
3. _____

My affirmations:

1. _____
2. _____
3. _____

"Gratitude is the fairest blossom which springs from the soul.
~ Henry Ward Beecher

Date _____

Today I am thankful for:

1. _____
2. _____
3. _____

My dreams and goals:

1. _____
2. _____
3. _____

What I love about myself:

1. _____
2. _____
3. _____

My affirmations:

1. _____
2. _____
3. _____

"No duty is more urgent than that of returning thanks." ~ James Allen

Date _____

Today I am thankful for:

1. _____
2. _____
3. _____

My dreams and goals:

1. _____
2. _____
3. _____

What I love about myself:

1. _____
2. _____
3. _____

My affirmations:

1. _____
2. _____
3. _____

"Let us be grateful to people who make us happy, they are the charming gardeners who make our souls blossom." ~ Marcel Proust

Date _____

Today I am thankful for:

1. _____
2. _____
3. _____

My dreams and goals:

1. _____
2. _____
3. _____

What I love about myself:

1. _____
2. _____
3. _____

My affirmations:

1. _____
2. _____
3. _____

"The essence of all beautiful art, all great art, is gratitude." ~ Friedrich Nietzsche

Date _____

Today I am thankful for:

1. _____
2. _____
3. _____

My dreams and goals:

1. _____
2. _____
3. _____

What I love about myself:

1. _____
2. _____
3. _____

My affirmations:

1. _____
2. _____
3. _____

"It's not what happens to you, but how you react to it that matters." ~ Epictetus

Date _____

Today I am thankful for:

1. _____
2. _____
3. _____

My dreams and goals:

1. _____
2. _____
3. _____

What I love about myself:

1. _____
2. _____
3. _____

My affirmations:

1. _____
2. _____
3. _____

"Happiness is a habit—cultivate it." ~ Elbert Hubbard

Date _____

Today I am thankful for:

1. _____
2. _____
3. _____

My dreams and goals:

1. _____
2. _____
3. _____

What I love about myself:

1. _____
2. _____
3. _____

My affirmations:

1. _____
2. _____
3. _____

"Wonder is the desire for knowledge." ~ Thomas Aquinas

Date _____

Today I am thankful for:

1. _____
2. _____
3. _____

My dreams and goals:

1. _____
2. _____
3. _____

What I love about myself:

1. _____
2. _____
3. _____

My affirmations:

1. _____
2. _____
3. _____

"You are today where your thoughts have brought you." ~ James Allen

Date _____

Today I am thankful for:

1. _____

2. _____

3. _____

My dreams and goals:

1. _____

2. _____

3. _____

What I love about myself:

1. _____

2. _____

3. _____

My affirmations:

1. _____

2. _____

3. _____

"A man is literally what he thinks." ~ James Allen

Date _____

Today I am thankful for:

1. _____
2. _____
3. _____

My dreams and goals:

1. _____
2. _____
3. _____

What I love about myself:

1. _____
2. _____
3. _____

My affirmations:

1. _____
2. _____
3. _____

"Dream lofty dreams, and as you dream, so you shall become, your vision is the promise of what you shall one day be." ~ James Allen

Date _____

Today I am thankful for:

1. _____
2. _____
3. _____

My dreams and goals:

1. _____
2. _____
3. _____

What I love about myself:

1. _____
2. _____
3. _____

My affirmations:

1. _____
2. _____
3. _____

"A person is only by the thoughts that he chooses." ~ James Allen

Date _____

Today I am thankful for:

1. _____
2. _____
3. _____

My dreams and goals:

1. _____
2. _____
3. _____

What I love about myself:

1. _____
2. _____
3. _____

My affirmations:

1. _____
2. _____
3. _____

"As a man thinketh in his heart, so shall he be." ~ James Allen

Date _____

Today I am thankful for:

1. _____
2. _____
3. _____

My dreams and goals:

1. _____
2. _____
3. _____

What I love about myself:

1. _____
2. _____
3. _____

My affirmations:

1. _____
2. _____
3. _____

"All that a man achieves and all that he fails to achieve is the direct result of his own thoughts." ~ James Allen

Date _____

Today I am thankful for:

1. _____
2. _____
3. _____

My dreams and goals:

1. _____
2. _____
3. _____

What I love about myself:

1. _____
2. _____
3. _____

My affirmations:

1. _____
2. _____
3. _____

"Our life is what our thoughts make it." ~ James Allen

Date _____

Today I am thankful for:

1. _____
2. _____
3. _____

My dreams and goals:

1. _____
2. _____
3. _____

What I love about myself:

1. _____
2. _____
3. _____

My affirmations:

1. _____
2. _____
3. _____

"He is greatest whose strength carries up the most hearts by attraction of his own."
~ Henry Ward Beecher

Date _____

Today I am thankful for:

1. _____
2. _____
3. _____

My dreams and goals:

1. _____
2. _____
3. _____

What I love about myself:

1. _____
2. _____
3. _____

My affirmations:

1. _____
2. _____
3. _____

"Gratitude is the fairest blossom which springs from the soul.
~ Henry Ward Beecher

Date _____

Today I am thankful for:

1. _____
2. _____
3. _____

My dreams and goals:

1. _____
2. _____
3. _____

What I love about myself:

1. _____
2. _____
3. _____

My affirmations:

1. _____
2. _____
3. _____

"No duty is more urgent than that of returning thanks." ~ James Allen

Date _____

Today I am thankful for:

1. _____
2. _____
3. _____

My dreams and goals:

1. _____
2. _____
3. _____

What I love about myself:

1. _____
2. _____
3. _____

My affirmations:

1. _____
2. _____
3. _____

"Let us be grateful to people who make us happy, they are the charming gardeners who make our souls blossom." ~ Marcel Proust

Date _____

Today I am thankful for:

1. _____
2. _____
3. _____

My dreams and goals:

1. _____
2. _____
3. _____

What I love about myself:

1. _____
2. _____
3. _____

My affirmations:

1. _____
2. _____
3. _____

"The essence of all beautiful art, all great art, is gratitude." ~ Friedrich Nietzsche

Date _____

Today I am thankful for:

1. _____
2. _____
3. _____

My dreams and goals:

1. _____
2. _____
3. _____

What I love about myself:

1. _____
2. _____
3. _____

My affirmations:

1. _____
2. _____
3. _____

"It's not what happens to you, but how you react to it that matters." ~ Epictetus

Date _____

Today I am thankful for:

1. _____
2. _____
3. _____

My dreams and goals:

1. _____
2. _____
3. _____

What I love about myself:

1. _____
2. _____
3. _____

My affirmations:

1. _____
2. _____
3. _____

"Happiness is a habit—cultivate it." ~ Elbert Hubbard

Date _____

Today I am thankful for:

1. _____
2. _____
3. _____

My dreams and goals:

1. _____
2. _____
3. _____

What I love about myself:

1. _____
2. _____
3. _____

My affirmations:

1. _____
2. _____
3. _____

"Wonder is the desire for knowledge." ~ Thomas Aquinas

Date _____

Today I am thankful for:

1. _____
2. _____
3. _____

My dreams and goals:

1. _____
2. _____
3. _____

What I love about myself:

1. _____
2. _____
3. _____

My affirmations:

1. _____
2. _____
3. _____

"You are today where your thoughts have brought you." ~ James Allen

Date _____

Today I am thankful for:

1. _____
2. _____
3. _____

My dreams and goals:

1. _____
2. _____
3. _____

What I love about myself:

1. _____
2. _____
3. _____

My affirmations:

1. _____
2. _____
3. _____

"A man is literally what he thinks." ~ James Allen

Date _____

Today I am thankful for:

1. _____
2. _____
3. _____

My dreams and goals:

1. _____
2. _____
3. _____

What I love about myself:

1. _____
2. _____
3. _____

My affirmations:

1. _____
2. _____
3. _____

"Dream lofty dreams, and as you dream, so you shall become, your vision is the promise of what you shall one day be." ~ James Allen

Date _____

Today I am thankful for:

1. _____
2. _____
3. _____

My dreams and goals:

1. _____
2. _____
3. _____

What I love about myself:

1. _____
2. _____
3. _____

My affirmations:

1. _____
2. _____
3. _____

"A person is only by the thoughts that he chooses." ~ James Allen

Date _____

Today I am thankful for:

1. _____

2. _____

3. _____

My dreams and goals:

1. _____

2. _____

3. _____

What I love about myself:

1. _____

2. _____

3. _____

My affirmations:

1. _____

2. _____

3. _____

"As a man thinketh in his heart, so shall he be." ~ James Allen

Date _____

Today I am thankful for:

1. _____
2. _____
3. _____

My dreams and goals:

1. _____
2. _____
3. _____

What I love about myself:

1. _____
2. _____
3. _____

My affirmations:

1. _____
2. _____
3. _____

"All that a man achieves and all that he fails to achieve is the direct result of his own thoughts." ~ James Allen

Date _____

Today I am thankful for:

1. _____
2. _____
3. _____

My dreams and goals:

1. _____
2. _____
3. _____

What I love about myself:

1. _____
2. _____
3. _____

My affirmations:

1. _____
2. _____
3. _____

"Our life is what our thoughts make it." ~ James Allen

Date _____

Today I am thankful for:

1. _____
2. _____
3. _____

My dreams and goals:

1. _____
2. _____
3. _____

What I love about myself:

1. _____
2. _____
3. _____

My affirmations:

1. _____
2. _____
3. _____

"He is greatest whose strength carries up the most hearts by attraction of his own."
~ Henry Ward Beecher

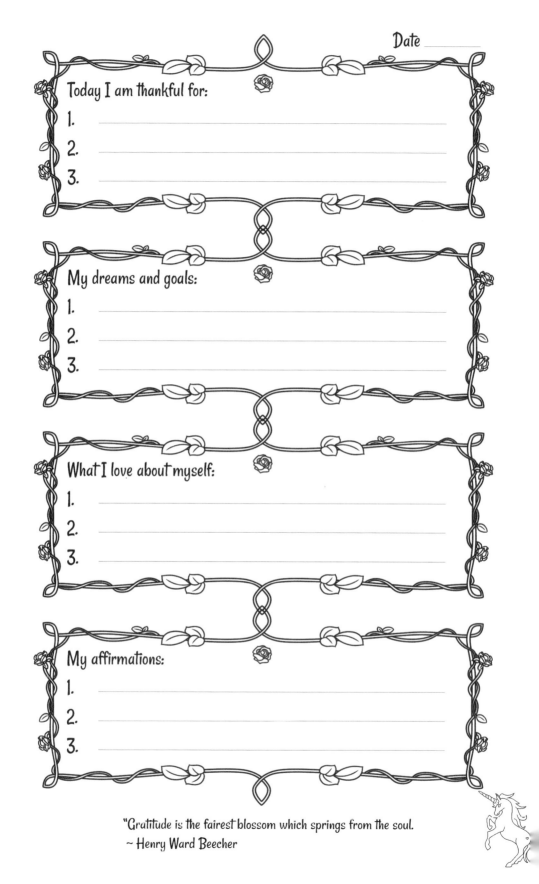

Date _____

Today I am thankful for:

1. _____
2. _____
3. _____

My dreams and goals:

1. _____
2. _____
3. _____

What I love about myself:

1. _____
2. _____
3. _____

My affirmations:

1. _____
2. _____
3. _____

"Gratitude is the fairest blossom which springs from the soul.
~ Henry Ward Beecher

Date _____

Today I am thankful for:

1. _____
2. _____
3. _____

My dreams and goals:

1. _____
2. _____
3. _____

What I love about myself:

1. _____
2. _____
3. _____

My affirmations:

1. _____
2. _____
3. _____

"No duty is more urgent than that of returning thanks." ~ James Allen

Date _____

Today I am thankful for:

1. _____

2. _____

3. _____

My dreams and goals:

1. _____

2. _____

3. _____

What I love about myself:

1. _____

2. _____

3. _____

My affirmations:

1. _____

2. _____

3. _____

"Let us be grateful to people who make us happy, they are the charming gardeners who make our souls blossom." ~ Marcel Proust

Date _____

Today I am thankful for:

1. _____

2. _____

3. _____

My dreams and goals:

1. _____

2. _____

3. _____

What I love about myself:

1. _____

2. _____

3. _____

My affirmations:

1. _____

2. _____

3. _____

"The essence of all beautiful art, all great art, is gratitude." ~ Friedrich Nietzsche

Date _____

Today I am thankful for:

1. _____
2. _____
3. _____

My dreams and goals:

1. _____
2. _____
3. _____

What I love about myself:

1. _____
2. _____
3. _____

My affirmations:

1. _____
2. _____
3. _____

"It's not what happens to you, but how you react to it that matters." ~ Epictetus

Date _____

Today I am thankful for:

1. _____
2. _____
3. _____

My dreams and goals:

1. _____
2. _____
3. _____

What I love about myself:

1. _____
2. _____
3. _____

My affirmations:

1. _____
2. _____
3. _____

"Happiness is a habit—cultivate it." ~ Elbert Hubbard

Date _____

Today I am thankful for:

1. _____
2. _____
3. _____

My dreams and goals:

1. _____
2. _____
3. _____

What I love about myself:

1. _____
2. _____
3. _____

My affirmations:

1. _____
2. _____
3. _____

"Wonder is the desire for knowledge." ~ Thomas Aquinas

Today I am thankful for:

1. _____
2. _____
3. _____

My dreams and goals:

1. _____
2. _____
3. _____

What I love about myself:

1. _____
2. _____
3. _____

My affirmations:

1. _____
2. _____
3. _____

"You are today where your thoughts have brought you." ~ James Allen

Date _____

Today I am thankful for:

1. _____
2. _____
3. _____

My dreams and goals:

1. _____
2. _____
3. _____

What I love about myself:

1. _____
2. _____
3. _____

My affirmations:

1. _____
2. _____
3. _____

"A man is literally what he thinks." ~ James Allen

Date _____

Today I am thankful for:

1. _____
2. _____
3. _____

My dreams and goals:

1. _____
2. _____
3. _____

What I love about myself:

1. _____
2. _____
3. _____

My affirmations:

1. _____
2. _____
3. _____

"Dream lofty dreams, and as you dream, so you shall become, your vision is the promise of what you shall one day be." ~ James Allen

Date _____

Today I am thankful for:

1. _____
2. _____
3. _____

My dreams and goals:

1. _____
2. _____
3. _____

What I love about myself:

1. _____
2. _____
3. _____

My affirmations:

1. _____
2. _____
3. _____

"A person is only by the thoughts that he chooses." ~ James Allen

Date _____

▷⟫⟫⟫➤ ➤⟫ • ⟪≪ ⟪⟪⟪◁ ◎ ▷⟫⟫⟫➤ ➤⟫ • ⟪≪ ⟪⟪⟪◁

Today I am thankful for:

1. _____

2. _____

3. _____

▷⟫⟫⟫➤ ➤⟫ • ⟪≪ ⟪⟪⟪◁ ◎ ▷⟫⟫⟫➤ ➤⟫ • ⟪≪ ⟪⟪⟪◁

My dreams and goals:

1. _____

2. _____

3. _____

▷⟫⟫⟫➤ ➤⟫ • ⟪≪ ⟪⟪⟪◁ ◎ ▷⟫⟫⟫➤ ➤⟫ • ⟪≪ ⟪⟪⟪◁

What I love about myself:

1. _____

2. _____

3. _____

▷⟫⟫⟫➤ ➤⟫ • ⟪≪ ⟪⟪⟪◁ ◎ ▷⟫⟫⟫➤ ➤⟫ • ⟪≪ ⟪⟪⟪◁

My affirmations:

1. _____

2. _____

3. _____

▷⟫⟫⟫➤ ➤⟫ • ⟪≪ ⟪⟪⟪◁ ◎ ▷⟫⟫⟫➤ ➤⟫ • ⟪≪ ⟪⟪⟪◁

"As a man thinketh in his heart, so shall he be." ~ James Allen

Date _____

Today I am thankful for:

1. _____
2. _____
3. _____

My dreams and goals:

1. _____
2. _____
3. _____

What I love about myself:

1. _____
2. _____
3. _____

My affirmations:

1. _____
2. _____
3. _____

"All that a man achieves and all that he fails to achieve is the direct result of his own thoughts." ~ James Allen

Date _____

Today I am thankful for:

1. _____

2. _____

3. _____

My dreams and goals:

1. _____

2. _____

3. _____

What I love about myself:

1. _____

2. _____

3. _____

My affirmations:

1. _____

2. _____

3. _____

"Our life is what our thoughts make it." ~ James Allen

Date _____

Today I am thankful for:

1. _____
2. _____
3. _____

My dreams and goals:

1. _____
2. _____
3. _____

What I love about myself:

1. _____
2. _____
3. _____

My affirmations:

1. _____
2. _____
3. _____

"He is greatest whose strength carries up the most hearts by attraction of his own."
~ Henry Ward Beecher

Date _____

Today I am thankful for:

1. _____
2. _____
3. _____

My dreams and goals:

1. _____
2. _____
3. _____

What I love about myself:

1. _____
2. _____
3. _____

My affirmations:

1. _____
2. _____
3. _____

"Gratitude is the fairest blossom which springs from the soul.
~ Henry Ward Beecher

Date _____

Today I am thankful for:

1. _____
2. _____
3. _____

My dreams and goals:

1. _____
2. _____
3. _____

What I love about myself:

1. _____
2. _____
3. _____

My affirmations:

1. _____
2. _____
3. _____

"No duty is more urgent than that of returning thanks." ~ James Allen